Magical Unicorn
ORIGAMI

ARCTURUS

This edition published in 2020 by Arcturus Publishing Limited
26/27 Bickels Yard, 151-153 Bermondsey Street,
London SE1 3HA

Author: Joe Fullman
Illustrator: Sam Loman
Editor: Penny Worms
Designer: Duck Egg Blue
Models and photography: Belinda Webster and Michael Wiles

ISBN: 978-1-78950-256-5
CH007090NT
Supplier 26, Date 0120, Print run 9463

Printed in China

Contents

Introduction 4

Getting Started 5
Basic Folds..............5
Reverse Folds 6
Kite Base................7
Waterbomb Base........8

Unicorns Everywhere.....9

Unicorn Bookmark 10
Magical Unicorn...............12
Unicorn Brooch................16
Little Unicorn.................22
Unicorn Cake Topper.........28

Unicorn Magic............31

Fairy Friend 32
Enchanted Crown.............38
Giant Jewel 40
Flying Heart.................44
Magic Bracelet 46
Super Star 50

Unicorn Meadow..........53

Magic Flower...............54
Cute Cactus.................58
Toadstool Seat 62
Fluttering Butterfly............64
Beautiful Bird..................66
Magical Tent 70

Unicorn Picnic.............73

Ice Cream 74
Watermelon 76
Ice Pop....................78
Strawberry..................84
Treat Box..................88
Cupcake....................94

Introduction

Let's explore the wonderful world of unicorn origami. In this book, you'll learn how to make an awesome assortment of origami unicorns as well as models of their magical friends and some delightful treats for a unicorn picnic.

In traditional origami, the models are usually made from a single sheet of folded paper with no cutting or gluing involved. We've broken the rules here and there to make our models as magical as possible.

Ask an adult to help with any projects that need scissors and glue. Otherwise, all you need to get started is a square of paper and your fingers. If you haven't made origami models before, try some of the easy projects first. Now, let's get ready for some unicorn folding!

Getting Started

The paper used in origami is thin but strong, so that it can be folded many times. You can use ordinary scrap paper, as long as it's not too thick.

A lot of these origami models are made with the same folds and basic starting designs, known as "bases." This introduction explains some of the ones that will appear most, so it's a good idea to master these before you start. When making the projects, follow the key to find out what the lines and arrows mean. And always crease well!

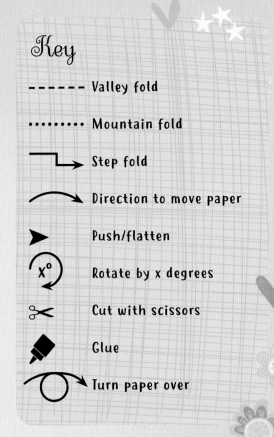
Basic Folds

Valley Fold

To make a valley fold, fold the edges of the paper toward you, so that the crease is pointing down, like a valley.

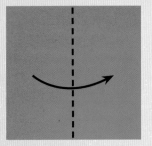

Mountain Fold

To make a mountain fold, fold the edges of the paper away from you, so that the crease is pointing up, like a mountain.

Step Fold

A step fold is used to make a step or zigzag in the paper.

1

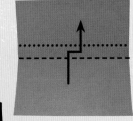

Valley fold the paper in half. Then make a mountain fold directly above the valley fold.

2

FLATTEN

Push the mountain fold over the valley fold and press down flat.

3

You now have a step fold. You can also make it in reverse, with the mountain fold first.

5

Reverse Folds

Inside Reverse Fold

This is useful if you want to flatten part of an origami model. It's a good way to create legs and horns for your unicorns.

1

Fold a piece of paper diagonally in half, as shown. Make a valley fold on one point and crease.

2

It's important to make sure that the paper is creased well. Run your finger over the crease two or three times.

3

Unfold, and then turn the crease you've just made into a mountain fold. Unfold, and open up the corner slightly.

OPEN

4

Open up the paper a little more and then tuck the tip of the point inside. Close the paper. This is the view from the underside of the paper.

5

Flatten the paper. You now have an inside reverse fold.

Outside Reverse Fold

This is great if you want to make part of your model stick out. It will come in handy for making heads and tails.

1

Fold a piece of paper diagonally in half, as shown. Make a valley fold on one point and crease.

2

It's important to make sure that the paper is creased well. Run your finger over the crease two or three times.

3

Unfold, and then turn the crease you've just made into a mountain fold. Unfold, and open up the corner slightly.

OPEN

4

Open up the paper a little more and start to turn the corner inside out. Then close the paper when the fold begins to turn.

5

Flatten the paper. You now have an outside reverse fold.

Kite Base

1

Place your paper like this. Valley fold it in half from left to right.

2

Valley fold the left-hand point over to the middle crease.

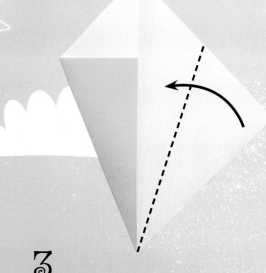

3

Repeat step 2 on the other side.

4

You now have a kite base.

Waterbomb Base

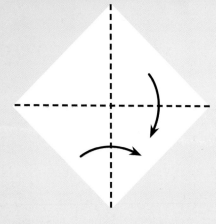

1

Start with a corner facing you. Valley fold from top to bottom and unfold. Then valley fold from left to right and unfold.

TURN OVER

45°

2

Turn your paper over and rotate it so that a straight edge is facing you.

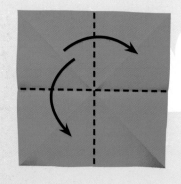

3

Valley fold from top to bottom and unfold. Then valley fold from left to right and unfold.

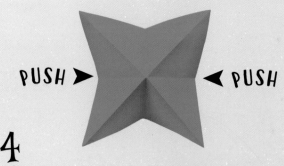

PUSH ► ◄ **PUSH**

4

Push the sides of the paper together, so the middle point pops up.

5

Keep pushing the sides in, bringing the back and front sections together.

FLATTEN

6

Flatten the paper down. You now have a waterbomb base.

Unicorns Everywhere

Where better to start than with the unicorns themselves? In this chapter, you'll learn how to make unicorns both big and small—in fact, you could make your own unicorn family—as well as some great unicorn-themed projects, including a brooch, a cake topper, and a cute little unicorn bookmark.

Unicorn Bookmark

Let's start by making a unicorn bookmark—that way you'll know exactly what project to turn to in this book.

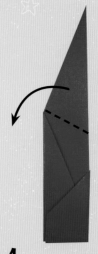

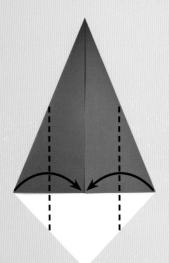

1
Start with a kite base (see page 7) placed this way up. Valley fold the left- and right-hand points over to the central line.

2
Valley fold up the bottom point, as shown.

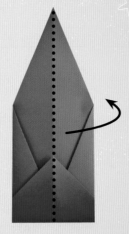

3
Mountain fold the paper in half from right to left.

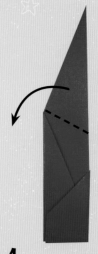

4
Valley fold the top point down and to the left.

5
Valley fold the point back to the right.

6
Make one farther small valley fold, taking the point back over to the left.

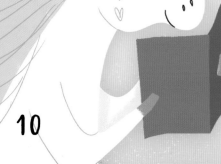

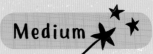
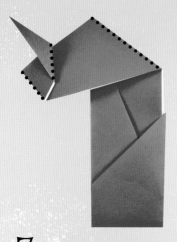

7

Your paper should look like this. Unfold the folds you made in steps 4 to 6 and fold them the other way, so they're also mountain folds, then unfold.

8

Turn the fold you made in step 4 into an inside reverse fold (see page 6).

9

Turn the fold you made in step 5 into an inside reverse fold.

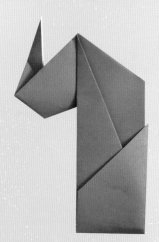

10

Turn the fold you made in step 6 into an inside reverse fold. This is the horn.

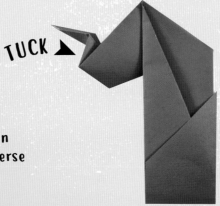

TUCK ▲

11

Tuck the horn inside the head so it sticks straight up.

12

Add a friendly face to your unicorn, then find a book it can call home.

11

Magical Unicorn

Follow these instructions to make a special unicorn with a long horn filled with magic.

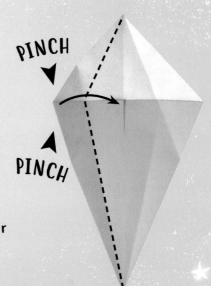

1
Start with a kite base (see page 7) like this. Fold the top-left and top-right edges over to the central crease.

2
Unfold the folds you made in step 1.

UNFOLD   UNFOLD

3
Now fold the left and right bottom edges over to the central crease.

4
Unfold the folds you made in step 3.

UNFOLD   UNFOLD

5
On the left-hand side, start folding the top left-edge and the bottom left edge toward the central crease along the creases you made in step 1 and step 3. As you fold, pinch the paper either side of the left-hand point.

PINCH

PINCH

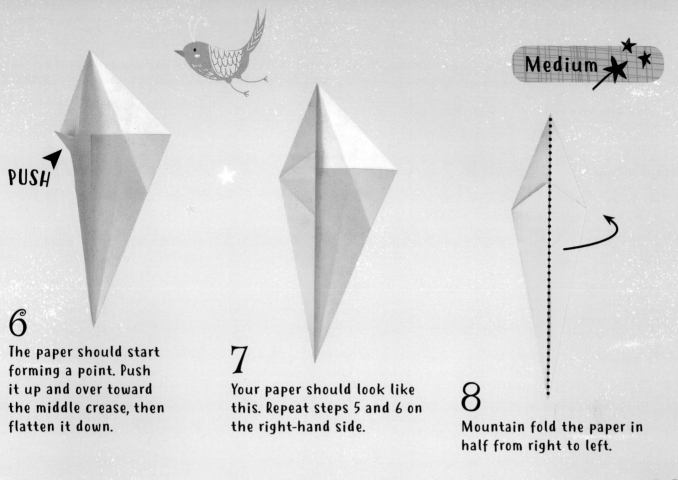

PUSH

6

The paper should start forming a point. Push it up and over toward the middle crease, then flatten it down.

7

Your paper should look like this. Repeat steps 5 and 6 on the right-hand side.

8

Mountain fold the paper in half from right to left.

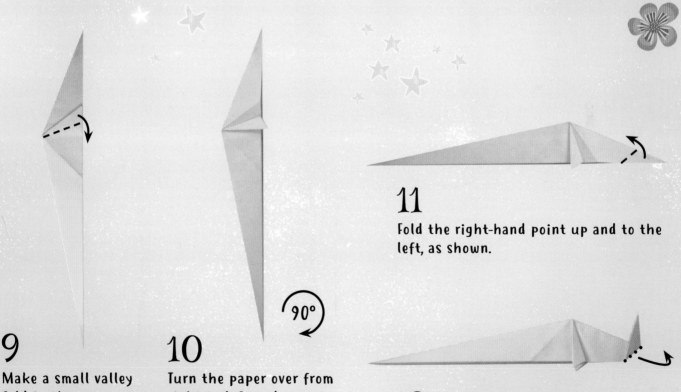

11

Fold the right-hand point up and to the left, as shown.

9

Make a small valley fold in the upper flap, as shown.

10

Turn the paper over from right to left and repeat step 9 on that side. Then turn the paper over again from right to left, and rotate it to the right.

90°

12

Fold it the other way, so it's also a mountain fold, then turn it into an inside reverse fold (see page 6).

13

13

Make a small mountain fold on the right. Fold it the other way, so it's also a valley fold, then turn it into an inside reverse fold.

14

Mountain fold the left-hand point up and to the right. Fold it the other way, so it's also a valley fold, then turn it into an inside reverse fold.

15

Flatten your paper down until it looks like the picture in step 16.

FLATTEN FLATTEN

16

Mountain fold the top point down and to the left. Fold it the other way, so it's also a valley fold, then turn it into an inside reverse fold.

17

Flatten your paper down.

FLATTEN

FLATTEN

18

Mountain fold the left-hand point back to the right. Fold it the other way, so it's also a valley fold, then turn it into an inside reverse fold.

FLATTEN

FLATTEN

19
Flatten your paper down.

PULL

20
Pull the top right-hand point up and to the left slightly.

21
Mountain fold the right-hand point up and to the left so it sticks straight up. Fold it the other way, so it's also a valley fold, then turn it into an inside reverse fold.

TUCK

FLATTEN

FLATTEN

22
Your paper should look like this. Flatten the paper down and make sure the horn is tucked inside the head.

24
Give your unicorn a happy expression—it's ready to start playing with its friends.

OPEN ▶

23
Open up your model slightly at the bottom and your unicorn should be able to stand up.

Unicorn Brooch

How would you like to wear your very own unicorn? You'll need a safety pin to complete this project.

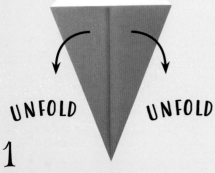

UNFOLD **UNFOLD**

1
Start with a kite base (see page 7) placed this way up. Unfold the left- and right-hand sides.

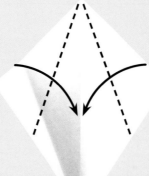

2
Make a kite base the other way up by folding the top-left and the top-right edges over to the central line.

3
Make a valley fold along the crease, as shown. As you do, lift the bottom left point of the right-hand flap and bring it up in line with the central crease.

◄ FLATTEN

4
As you bring the point up, the right-hand side of the paper should fold over to the middle creating a new flap. Flatten the paper down.

5
Your paper should look like this with a straight horizontal edge at the top of the new flap. Repeat steps 3 and 4 on the left-hand side.

TURN OVER

6
Turn your paper over from left to right.

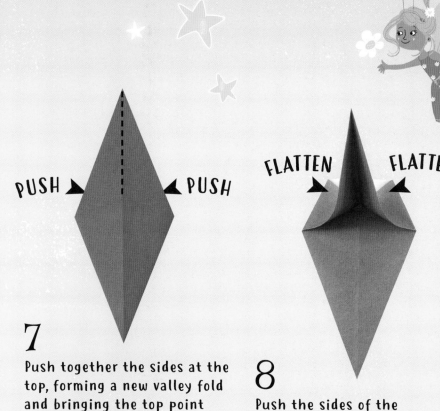

PUSH ► ◄ **PUSH**

7
Push together the sides at the top, forming a new valley fold and bringing the top point forward toward you.

FLATTEN ► ◄ **FLATTEN**

8
Push the sides of the pointed flap together and flatten the paper, so the flap is pointing toward you.

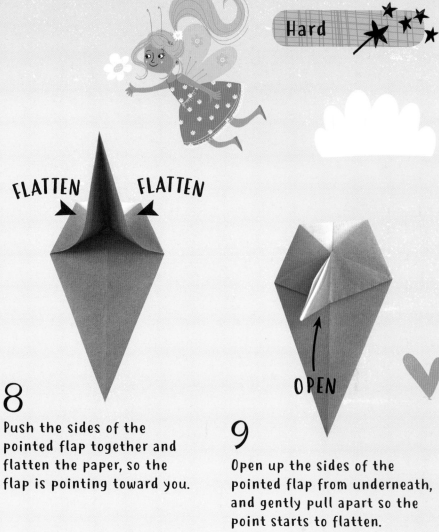

OPEN

9
Open up the sides of the pointed flap from underneath, and gently pull apart so the point starts to flatten.

PUSH ▼

10
Now push down on top of the flap, squashing it down onto the paper to form a triangle shape.

11
Your paper should look like this. Turn it over from left to right.

TURN OVER

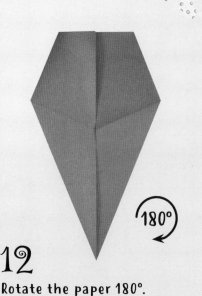

180°

12
Rotate the paper 180°.

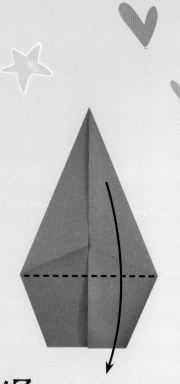

13

Valley fold the top point down, as shown.

14

Turn the paper over from left to right.

TURN OVER

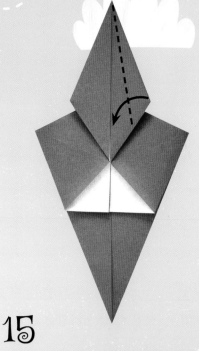

15

Make a small valley fold at the top on the right-hand side, as shown, so the right edge meets the central crease.

16

Repeat step 15 on the left-hand side.

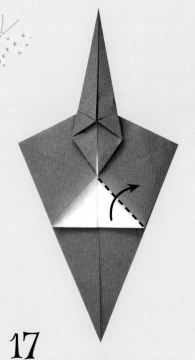

17

Valley fold the white triangle on the right-hand side.

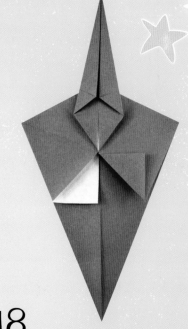

18

Repeat step 17 on the left-hand side.

19

Unfold the folds you made in steps 17 and 18.

TUCK INSIDE

20

Tuck the white triangle on the right-hand side under the flap above it.

TUCK

21

Make sure the triangle goes all the way in.

22

Repeat steps 20 and 21 on the left-hand side.

23

Valley fold the upper right-hand flap, as shown, so that the point overlaps the top edge. This is one of your unicorn's ears.

24

Repeat step 23 on the left-hand side.

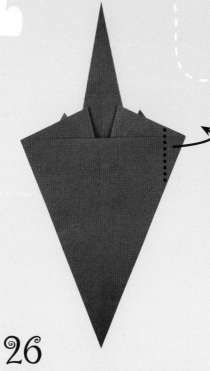

TURN OVER

25
Turn the paper over from left to right.

26
Mountain fold the right-hand point, as shown.

27
Repeat step 26 on the left-hand side.

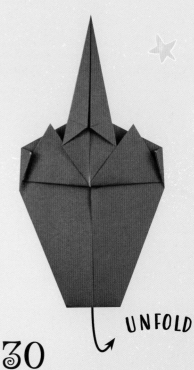

TURN OVER

UNFOLD

28
Valley fold the bottom point, as shown.

29
Turn the paper over from left to right.

30
Unfold the fold you made in step 28, bringing the point down to the bottom.

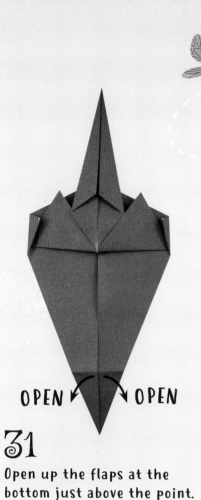

OPEN ↙ ↘ OPEN

31
Open up the flaps at the bottom just above the point.

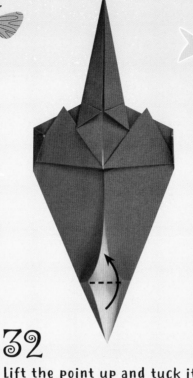

32
Lift the point up and tuck it under the flaps you opened in step 31.

FLATTEN ► ◄ FLATTEN

33
Flatten down the flaps on both sides over the point.

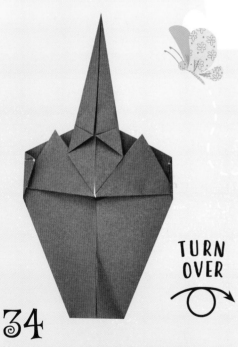

TURN OVER

34
Your paper should look like this. Ask a grown-up to fix a safety pin to this side of the paper, then turn it over from left to right.

35
Give your unicorn a happy expression and it's ready to wear.

21

Little Unicorn

This cute unicorn is ready to join its friends in a magical forest. Why not make it a few brothers and sisters too using different types of paper?

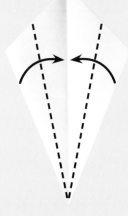

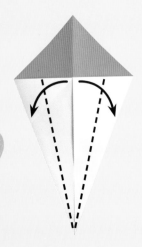

1

Make a kite base (see page 7) but start with the white side facing down so your paper ends up looking like this. Make two valley folds in the upper layer on both sides.

TURN OVER

2

Turn your paper over from left to right.

3

Make valley folds on either side, as shown, so that the edges line up with the central crease. Be sure to fold all layers.

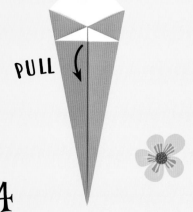

PULL

4

Open up the upper left-hand flap and pull its top-right point down so it begins to form a triangle shape.

FLATTEN

5

Your paper should look like this. Keep the point in line with the central crease and flatten the triangle shape down.

6

Repeat steps 4 and 5 on the right-hand side.

7
Valley fold the top left-hand edge over to the central crease.

8
Repeat step 7 on the right-hand side.

UNFOLD   UNFOLD

9
Open out the folds you made in steps 7 and 8.

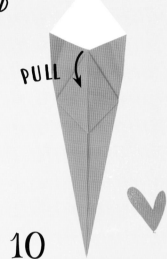

PULL

10
Open out the top left flap and, as with step 4, pull its top-right point down so it begins to form a triangle shape.

PULL

11
Keep pulling the point down in line with the central crease so the triangle shape goes over the flap you made in steps 4 and 5.

12
Repeat steps 10 and 11 on the right-hand side.

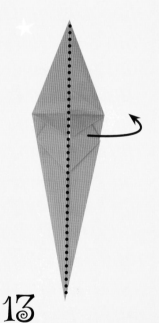

13
Mountain fold the paper in half from right to left.

OPEN

OPEN → ABOVE THIS POINT

14
Open out the top left-hand side of the paper above the left-hand point of the triangle-shaped flaps you made in steps 4 to 6. Rotate the open side toward you.

PINCH ▶ ◀ **PINCH**

OPEN ↷

15

Pinch the top of the paper closed and open the paper out wide either side of the triangle shaped flaps.

PUSH ▶ ◀ **PUSH**

16

Push each side down and around the triangle shaped flaps at an angle. Flatten the paper down and rotate it clockwise so it lies flat.

↻ 90°

17

Your paper should look like this. Rotate it to the right.

18

Make a mountain fold as shown—note that the fold goes in between the two small triangle flaps you made in steps 4 to 6. Fold it the other way, so it's also a valley fold, then turn it into an inside reverse fold (see page 6).

THE FOLD GOES UNDER THE UPPER LAYER

FLATTEN ◀

◀ **FLATTEN**

19

Flatten your paper down.

20

Make a mountain fold as shown on the left-hand point. Fold it the other way, so it's also a valley fold, then turn it into an inside reverse fold.

FLATTEN ◀   ◀ **FLATTEN**

21

Flatten your paper down.

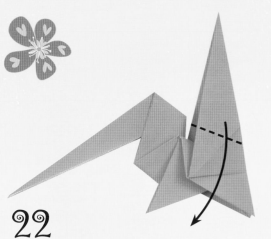

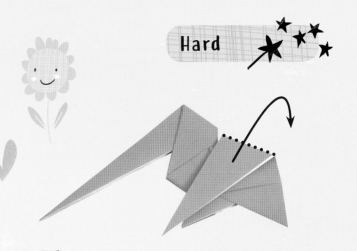

22

Valley fold the top right point down and to the left at an angle, as shown.

23

Fold it the other way, so it's also a mountain fold, then unfold.

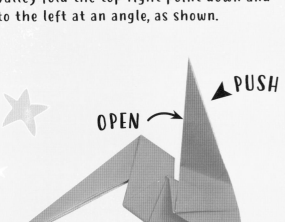

PUSH

OPEN

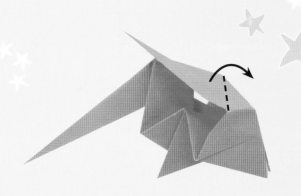

24

Open up the right-hand flap on the left side and push it down to the left so it forms a flat kite shape.

25

Make a valley fold over to the right at the widest point of the kite shape.

PUSH

PUSH

26

Push together the sides of the flat triangle shape you made in step 25. This should create a valley fold along its length. Flatten it down.

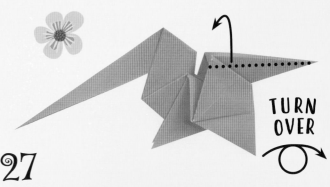

TURN OVER

27

Your paper should look like this. Make a small mountain fold in the upper layer of the new right-hand point, as shown. Turn your paper over from left to right.

25

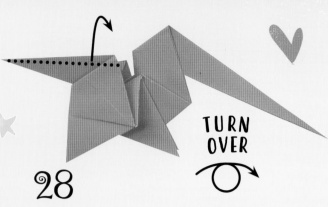

28

Repeat step 27 on this side, then turn the paper over again.

TURN OVER

29

Make a valley fold in the right-hand point.

30

Fold it the other way, so it's also a mountain fold, then turn it into an outside reverse fold (see page 6).

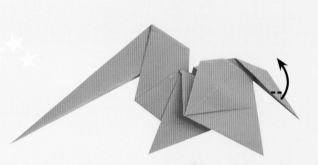

31

Make another small valley fold nearer the end of the point.

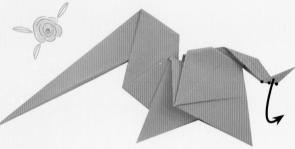

32

Fold it the other way, so it's also a mountain fold, then turn this into an outside reverse fold too.

OPEN

33

Open out the left-hand point. This will form the head, while the vertical piece in the middle will be the neck.

PUSH

PUSH

34

With the left-hand point opened at the top, push one side round the back of the neck and the other side round the front, as shown, so the point raises up.

 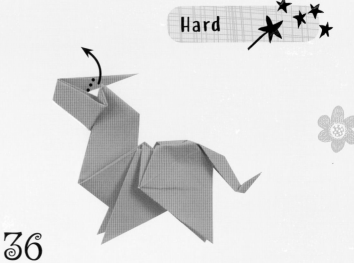
35

Make a mountain fold in the left-hand point, as shown.

36

Make a mountain fold as shown, so the point sticks straight up.

37

This is what your paper should look like from behind.

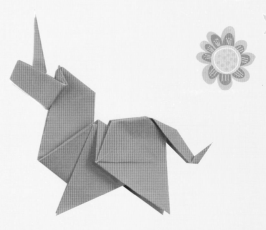

38

Unfold the folds you made in steps 35 and 36, and fold them the other way, so they're also valley folds. Then turn them into two inside-reverse folds, one inside the other to form the head and horn.

TUCK ▶

39

Make sure the horn is tucked into the head.

40

Your little unicorn is ready for its first gallop. Add some sparkly patterns!

Unicorn Cake Topper

Unicorns love parties, particularly ones with cake. You'll need three pieces of paper, scissors, glue, and a thin wooden stick for this project.

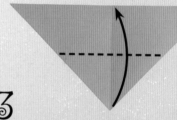

1
Start with your paper like this, white side up with a corner facing you. Valley fold it in half from left to right, then unfold.

2
Valley fold it in half from top to bottom.

3
Valley fold the bottom point up to the top edge. Be sure to fold both layers, then unfold.

4
Now fold just the upper layer of the bottom point up to the top edge, using the crease line you made in step 3.

5
Fold the right-hand point across and down to the bottom point.

6
Now fold the left-hand point across and down to the bottom point.

7
Unfold the folds you made in steps 5 and 6 about half way.

UNFOLD   UNFOLD

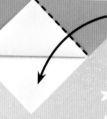

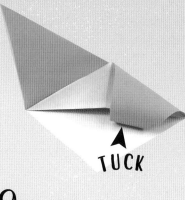

TUCK

8
Tuck the top right point under the white triangle-shaped flap in the middle of your model.

9
Keep tucking until the point can't go in any farther, then flatten the paper down.

10
Your paper should look like this. Repeat steps 8 and 9 on the left-hand side.

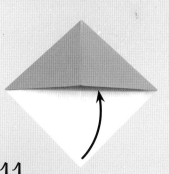

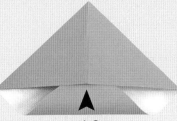
TUCK

TURN OVER

11
Tuck the bottom point up inside the top triangle.

12
Keep tucking until it can't go any farther, then flatten the paper down.

13
Your paper should look like this. Turn it over from left to right.

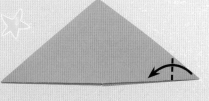

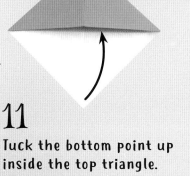

14
Make a small valley fold near the right-hand point, as shown.

15
Fold it the other way, so it's also a mountain fold, then turn it into an inside reverse fold (see page 6).

16
Make a small valley fold near the left-hand point. Fold it the other way, so it's also a mountain fold, then turn it into an inside reverse fold.

29

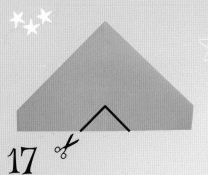

17

Cut out a small triangle-shaped section, as shown. Be sure to cut through all the layers.

18

Rotate your paper 45° to the left.

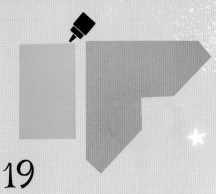

19

Take the second piece of paper and use scissors to cut a rectangle a little bit shorter than one side of your paper. Use a thin line of glue to attach it to the left-hand side of the first piece of paper.

20

Use scissors to cut the second piece of paper into several thin strips. This is the unicorn's mane.

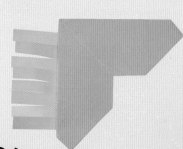

21

Your paper should look like this. Now use scissors to cut out a triangle shape from the third piece of paper. This is your horn.

22

Use a thin line of glue to stick the horn on top of the unicorn's head.

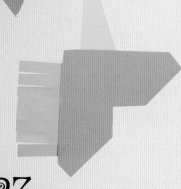

23

Your paper should look like this. Add features to your unicorn, then glue it to the top of your stick.

24

Your unicorn is ready for its first party. It's cake time!

30

Unicorn Magic

Let's explore more of the magical world of unicorns. We can meet their fairy friends and make some magical unicorn objects, including a crown, a bracelet, a flying heart, and giant sparkling jewels.

Fairy Friend

Unicorns aren't the only magical creatures in the forest. Here's how to make a fabulous fairy friend to flutter around with your unicorns.

1

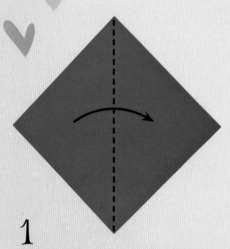

Start with your paper like this, white side down, with a corner facing you. Valley fold it in half from left to right, then unfold.

2

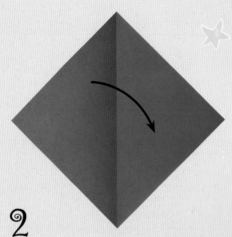

Valley fold the top-left edge over to the bottom right edge, but don't crease.

3

PRESS

Press down to make a small crease on the top edge of the paper in the position shown. Then unfold.

4

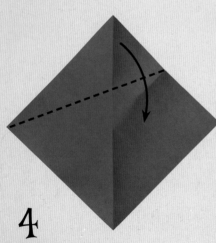

Make a valley fold between the small crease you made in step 3 and the left corner.

5

UNFOLD

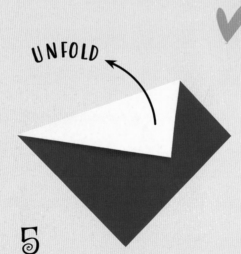

Unfold the fold you made in step 4.

6

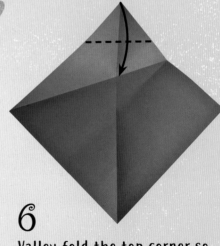

Valley fold the top corner so it touches the point where the crease you made in step 1 and the crease you made in step 4 meet.

UNFOLD

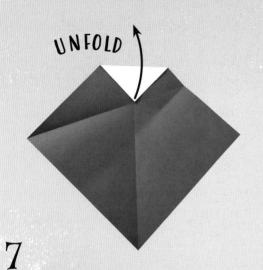

7

Unfold the fold you made in step 6.

8

Valley fold the bottom corner up to the top.

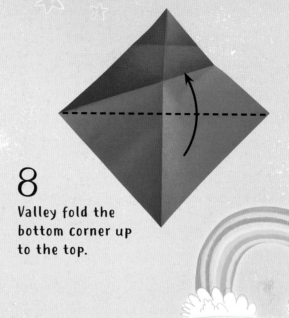

TURN
OVER

9

Your paper should look like this. Turn it over from left to right.

10

Valley fold the right-hand point up to the top point.

11

Repeat step 10 on the left-hand side.

TURN
OVER

12

Turn your paper over from left to right.

13

Valley fold the top point of the upper layer down to the bottom.

14

Fold over the top point of the next layer along the crease line you made in step 6.

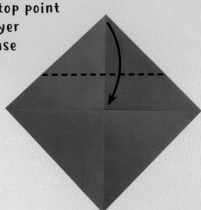

15

Turn your paper over from left to right.

TURN OVER

16

Unfold the folds you made in steps 10 and 11.

UNFOLD **UNFOLD**

17

Make a diagonal valley fold on the right-hand side. The top-right point should touch the central crease.

18

Your paper should look like this with a diagonal flap on the right-hand side with a white triangle at the top. Lift the white triangle a little so you can make another diagonal valley fold in the flap by turning the paper underneath the white triangle and pressing down (see image for step 19).

MAKE FOLD BENEATH THE WHITE TRIANGLE

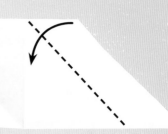

FLATTEN

19

Keep the white triangle in position, and fold the flap under it over to the central crease. Flatten the paper down.

UNFOLD

20

Your paper should look like this. Carefully unfold the folds you made in steps 17 to 19.

21

Make another diagonal fold on the right-hand side, using the lower crease line you made in step 19.

PULL

22

Open out the small white triangle at the top. Pull the right-hand side over to the right as you fold the left-hand side over the upper fold you made in step 19. Flatten the paper down.

23

Valley fold the bottom point up as shown until it forms a flap pointing straight up toward you.

24

Continue lifting the bottom point toward the top. As you do, the right-hand point should start coming over to the left. Flatten it down over the other point.

FLATTEN

25
Valley fold the top point over to the right until it begins to form a semi-spherical shape.

26

Flatten the paper down along the line shown.

FLATTEN ▶

27
Make a small valley fold on the right-hand side, as shown.

28
Your paper should look like this. Repeat steps 17 to 27 on the left-hand side.

29
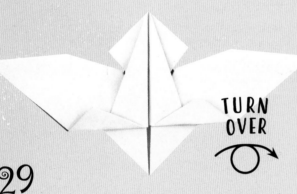
Turn your paper over from left to right.

TURN OVER

30

Make a small mountain fold in the top point.

31

Make three more small mountain folds, as shown, to form the face.

32
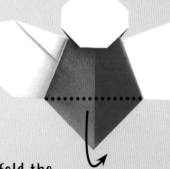
Mountain fold the bottom point of the upper layer and tuck it in.

33

Valley fold the bottom point that remains and tuck that in too.

34

Make a step fold in the right-hand wing, as shown (see page 5).

35

Make another step fold slightly farther along. Make sure the fold goes under the triangle at the top of the wing.

36

Make a third step fold to complete the wing.

37

Your paper should look like this. Repeat steps 34 to 36 on the left-hand side.

38

Give your fairy a happy expression. It's ready to play with the unicorns.

Enchanted Crown

Here's a crown fit for a unicorn—the royalty of the forest. It's also big enough for you to wear! You will need six pieces of paper for this project.

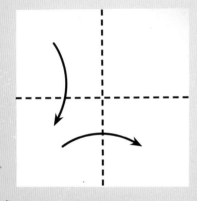

1

Place your first piece of paper like this, white side up with a straight edge facing you. Fold it in half from left to right, and unfold. Then fold it in half from top to bottom, and unfold.

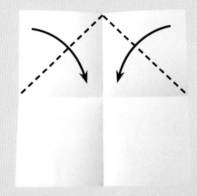

2

Fold the top left and the top right corners down to the central point.

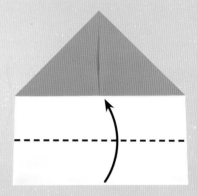

3

Fold the bottom edge up so it meets the bottom edge of the two triangular flaps.

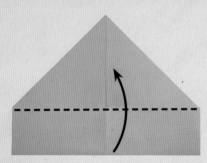

4

Fold the bottom edge up again along the line formed by the bottom edge of the two triangular flaps.

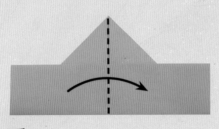

5

Fold the paper in half from left to right.

UNFOLD

6

Unfold the folds you made in steps 4 and 5.

38

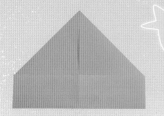

 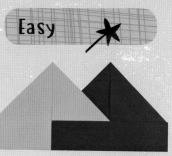
7

Your paper should look like this. Repeat steps 1 to 6 with your other pieces of paper.

8

SLIDE ➤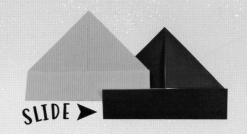

Take your first piece of paper and slide its right-hand bottom edge inside the bottom flap of the second piece of paper. Keep pushing until it's about half way across.

9

Your paper should look like this.

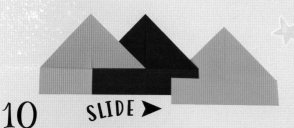

10

SLIDE ➤

Now slide the right-hand bottom edge of the second piece of paper inside the bottom flap of the third piece of paper. Keep pushing until it's about half way across.

11

Your paper should like this. Keep repeating the steps 8 to 10 until all six pieces of paper are joined together.

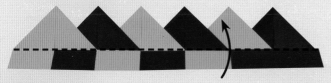

12

Fold over the bottom edge of all six pieces of paper at once, which will hold the pieces together.

13

Lift the six piece-model up and begin folding it round into a circle shape.

14

Slot one end into the other, just like you did with all the other pieces of paper.

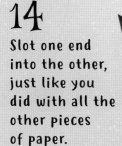

15

Time to decorate your crown with jewels and precious gems. Maybe you could stick a magic gem to the front (see pages 40-43)?

Giant Jewel

All unicorns like shiny precious gems, particularly ones as big and as full of magic as this one. You'll need three pieces of paper to complete this giant jewel.

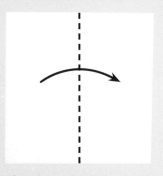

1

Take your first piece of paper and place it like this, white side up, with a straight edge facing you. Valley fold it in half from left to right, then unfold.

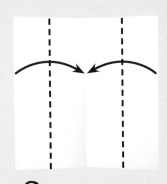

2

Valley fold the left- and right-hand edges over to the central crease.

UNFOLD   UNFOLD

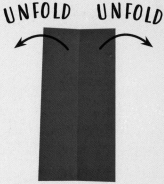

3

Unfold the folds you made in step 2.

4

Valley fold the bottom left and top right corners over to the crease lines you made in step 2.

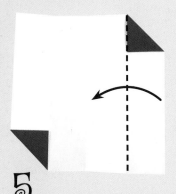

5

Refold the right-hand fold you made in step 2. Fold the paper over the triangle-shaped flap you made in step 4.

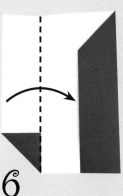

6

Repeat step 5 on the left-hand side.

7

Fold the top left point down and to the right so it lines up with the right-hand edge.

8

Now fold the bottom right point up and to the left so it lines up with the left-hand edge.

40

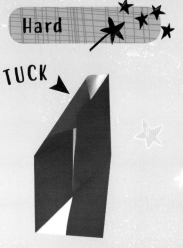
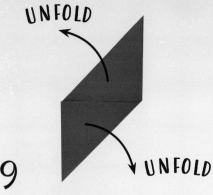

UNFOLD

UNFOLD

9

Unfold the folds you made in steps 7 and 8.

10

Take the top left point and fold it back over to the right edge, this time tucking it under the flap you made in step 5.

11

TUCK

Tuck the point right under the flap and flatten it down.

12

Your paper should look like this. Now do the same with the bottom right point. Fold it back over to the left edge, tucking it under the flap you made in step 6.

13

TUCK

Tuck the point right under the flap and flatten it down.

14

TURN OVER

Your paper should look like this. Turn it over from left to right.

15

45°

Rotate the paper 45° to the right.

16

Valley fold the top point down as shown.

17

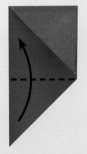

Valley fold the bottom point up.

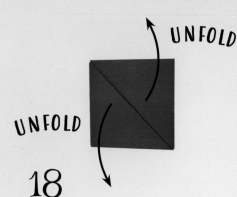

18

Unfold the folds you made in steps 16 and 17 part of the way, so the ends stick up toward you.

19

Your paper should look like this. Take the other two pieces of paper and repeat steps 1 to 18 with each, so you have three pieces folded the exact same way.

20

Take two of your pieces and position them like this. Slide the right-hand point of the left piece (red) inside the right piece (pink).

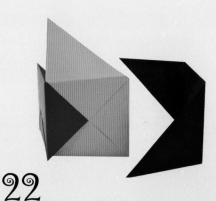

21

Keep pushing until it's all the way in.

22

Your pieces should look like this. Get your third piece and position it as shown.

23

Slide the point of the right (purple) piece into the other slot in the bottom of the pink piece, as shown, and keep pushing until it's all the way in.

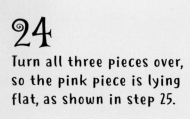

24

Turn all three pieces over, so the pink piece is lying flat, as shown in step 25.

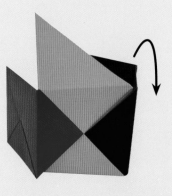

25

Take the top point of the red triangle and bring it down to touch the right corner of the pink piece. It twists the red piece slightly.

26

While holding the red piece in position, bring the top point of the purple piece over and tuck it inside the far flap of the red piece.

TUCK

27

Tuck it all the way in. The piece may bend or crumple a little, but you can straighten it out gently when it's fully tucked in.

28

Your paper should look like this. Fold the point nearest to you (from the central, pink piece) into the nearest purple flap.

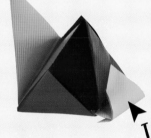

29

Tuck it right in.

TUCK

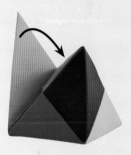

30

Fold the remaining pink point into the remaining red flap.

TUCK

31

Push it right in.

32

Your paper should look like this. Make sure all the flaps are tightly tucked, then position your jewel so it looks like the image in step 33.

33

Your jewel is ready. Why not fold some more to create your own treasure chest?

Flying Heart

In the world of unicorns, hearts have wings and can fly. Follow these simple instructions to make your own fluttering heart.

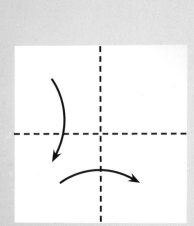

1

Place your paper like this. Valley fold it in half from left to right, and unfold. Then valley fold it in half from top to bottom, and unfold.

2

Valley fold the top edge down to the central crease.

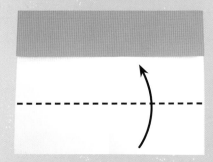

3

Valley fold the bottom edge up to the central crease.

4

Turn your paper over from left to right.

TURN OVER

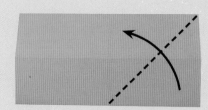

5

Valley fold the bottom right corner up and over to the central crease.

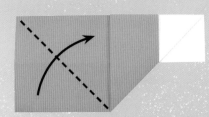

6

Repeat step 5 on the left-hand side.

7

Your paper should look like this. Turn it over from left to right.

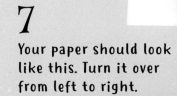

TURN OVER

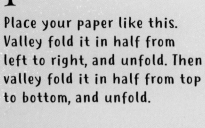

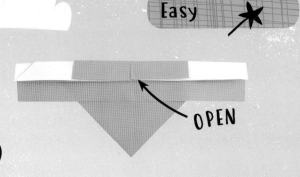

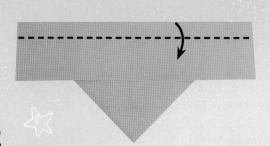

8

Valley fold over the top edge, as shown.

9

Open up the flap on the right-hand side.

OPEN

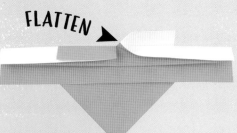

FLATTEN ▶

10

Flatten down the left-hand side of the flap to form a triangle shape.

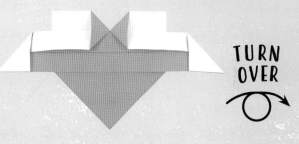

11

Your paper should look like this. Repeat steps 9 and 10 on the left-hand side.

12

Valley fold the left and right corners, as shown.

TURN OVER

13

Your paper should look like this. Turn it over from left to right.

14

Mountain fold the top left and top right corners, as shown.

15

Your flying heart is ready. But where will it flutter off to?

Magic Bracelet

This bracelet may be filled with magic. Once it's made, give it a quick rub and make a wish—it may just come true! You'll need scissors to complete this project.

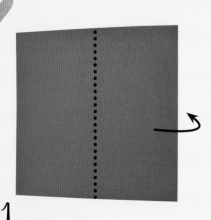

1

Place your paper like this, white side down, with a straight edge facing you. Mountain fold it in half from right to left, then unfold.

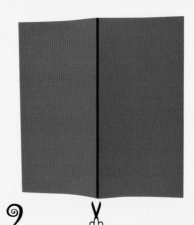

2

Carefully cut the paper in half along the fold line you made in step 1.

TURN OVER

3

Take one of the pieces of paper and turn it over from left to right.

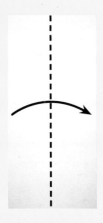

4

Valley fold it in half from left to right, then unfold.

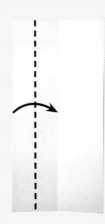

5

Valley fold the left-hand edge over to the central crease.

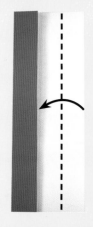

6

Repeat step 5 on the right-hand side.

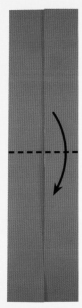

7

Your paper should look
like this. Valley fold it in
half from top to bottom.

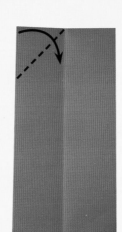

8

Valley fold the top-left corner
over to the central crease.

9

Fold it the other way so it's
also a mountain fold, then
turn it into an inside reverse
fold (see page 6).

◀ FLATTEN

10

Flatten the paper down.

11

Repeat steps 8 to 10 on the
right-hand side.

12

Valley fold the left-hand
edge of the upper layer over
to the central crease.

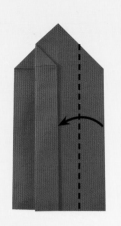

13

Repeat step 12 on the right-hand side.

14

Your paper should look like this. Turn it over from left to right.

TURN OVER

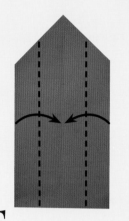

15

Now repeat steps 12 and 13 on this side.

16

Rotate the paper 90° to the right.

90°

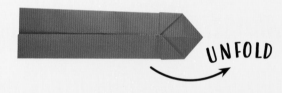

17

Unfold the bottom layer of the paper over to the right. As you do, the middle of the paper should form a pointed crown-like shape pointing up toward you.

UNFOLD

18

LIFT UP

Lift the middle section of the paper up slightly.

19

PUSH OUT

Put your finger inside the middle section and push out the folds so they form a cube-like shape.

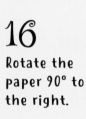

48

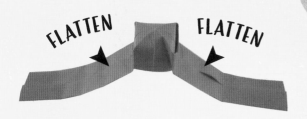

FLATTEN   FLATTEN

20

Your paper should look like this. Flatten down the flaps on either side again.

21

90°

Rotate the paper 90° to the left.

TURN OVER

22

Turn the paper over a quarter-turn from right to left.

23

Curl the bands around to form your bracelet.

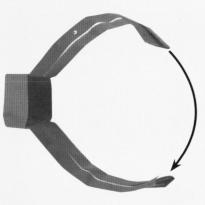

24

Fit one band inside the other.

25

Fasten the ends securely. You can use sticky tape if you want.

26

Your bracelet is ready. Decorate it with sparkly paint to bring out the magic.

Super Star

The best way to do magic is by using a wand. First, get a stick or straw around 30 cm (12 in) long to be your wand. Then follow these steps to make a magic-filled star to go on the end.

◄ FLATTEN

1

Start by making a waterbomb base (see page 8), then position your paper like this with the long edge facing you. Valley fold the right-hand point of the upper layer over to the left, but don't crease.

2

Your paper should look like this with three layers on the left and one on the right. Flatten the paper down.

3

Fold the top-left edge of the upper layer over to the central crease so that the left-hand corner points straight down.

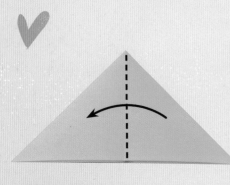

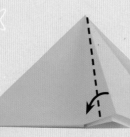

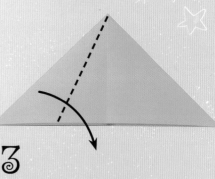

4

Bring the bottom point over to the right.

5

Make a new valley fold so that the crease you made in step 3 lines up with the central crease.

6

Valley fold the left-hand point of the next layer over to the right so it covers the flap you made in step 5.

7

Fold the top-right edge of that layer across so it lines up with the central crease and the right-hand corner points straight down.

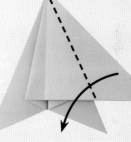

8

Bring the bottom point over to the left.

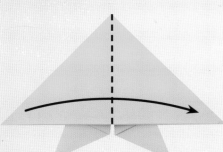

9

Repeat step 5 on this side, so the crease you made in step 7 lines up with the central crease.

TURN OVER

10

Your paper should look like this. Turn it over from left to right.

11

Fold the left-hand point all the way over to the right.

12

Fold the top-right edge of the upper layer down to the central crease so that the right-hand corner points straight down.

13

Unfold the folds you made in steps 11 and 12.

14

Make a valley fold so that the crease you made in step 12 lines up with the central crease.

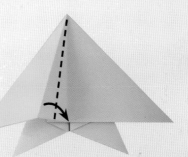

51

15

Valley fold the right-hand point all the way over to the left.

16

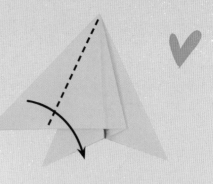

Valley fold the top left edge over to the central crease so that the left corner points straight down.

17

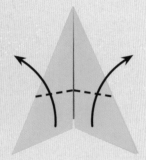

Unfold the folds you made in steps 15 and 16.

18

Make a valley fold so that the crease you made in step 16 lines up with the central crease.

19

Your paper should look like this. Make two valley folds on the upper layer, as shown, lifting the two points up and out to the side.

20

FLATTEN
FLATTEN FLATTEN
FLATTEN

The folds in the middle should lift up as you make the fold. Flatten them down to form a white square shape.

21

Your paper should look like this. Turn it over from left to right.

TURN
OVER

22

Your star is ready to be attached to a wand, or perhaps to the tip of a unicorn's horn.

Unicorn Meadow

Let's venture out into the Magical Meadow, where the unicorns spend their days frolicking in the grass. Help to fill it with flowers, butterflies, and birds by completing the projects on these pages.

Magic Flower

Unicorns love pretty flowers. You'll need glue and two pieces of paper for this project. One sheet of paper should be green, to make the stem.

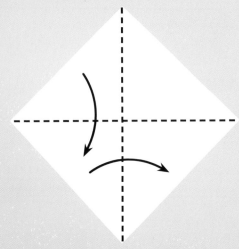

1
Start by making the flower. Place your non-green paper like this, white side up with a corner facing you. Valley fold in half from left to right, and unfold. Then valley fold in half from top to bottom, and unfold.

2
Turn the paper over from left to right.

TURN OVER

3
Valley fold the top corner down to the central crease.

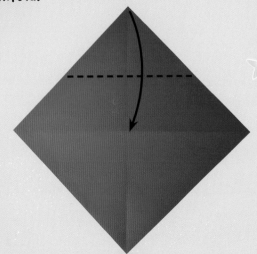

4
Valley fold the top edge down to the central crease.

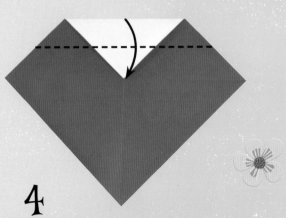

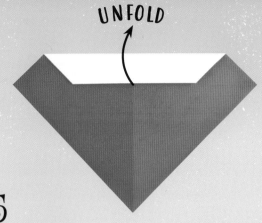

5

Unfold the folds you made in steps 3 and 4.

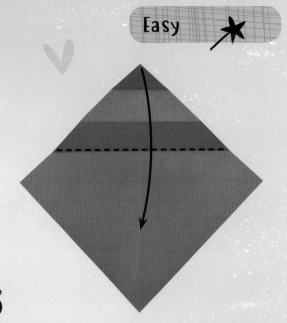

Easy ⭐

6

Valley fold the top corner down again along the line of the third crease line from the top.

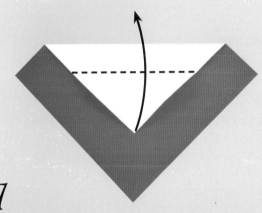

7

Valley fold the point back up again as shown, now using the first crease line from the top.

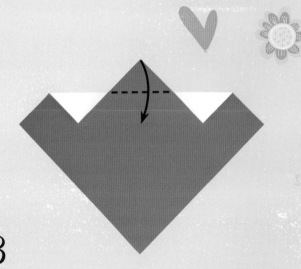

8

Valley fold the point down again using the remaining crease line.

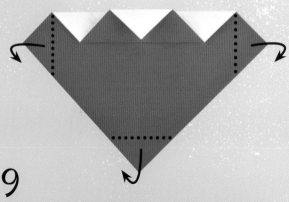

9

Mountain fold the left, right, and bottom points, as shown.

10

Your flower is ready. Put it to one side and get the green piece of paper so you can make the stalk.

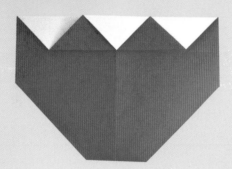

11

Place your paper like this, white side up with a corner facing you. Fold in half from left to right, then unfold.

12

Fold the paper in half from bottom to top.

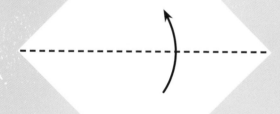

13

Fold the top right edge over to the central crease.

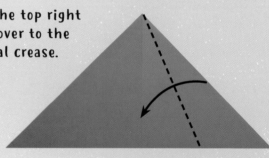

14

Repeat step 13 on the left-hand side.

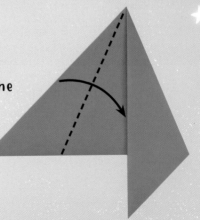

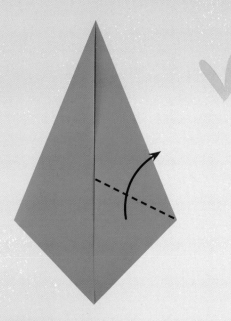

15

Valley fold the bottom right point up at an angle, as shown.

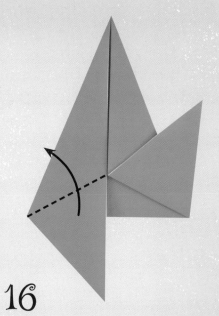

16

Repeat step 15 on the left-hand side.

17

Your paper should look like this. Get your flower and carefully attach it to the top of your stalk with glue.

18

That's one flower done. Why don't you make more for your unicorn meadow?

Cute Cactus

Follow these steps to create your own spiky cactus for the Magical Meadow to go alongside your flowers. You'll need a green piece of paper.

1
Start with a kite base (see page 7) placed like this. Valley fold the top left edge to the central crease.

2
Repeat step 1 on the right-hand side.

3
UNFOLD

Open up the fold you made in step 1.

4
PULL

Pull the middle point down along the central line, so that it forms a triangle-shaped flap.

58

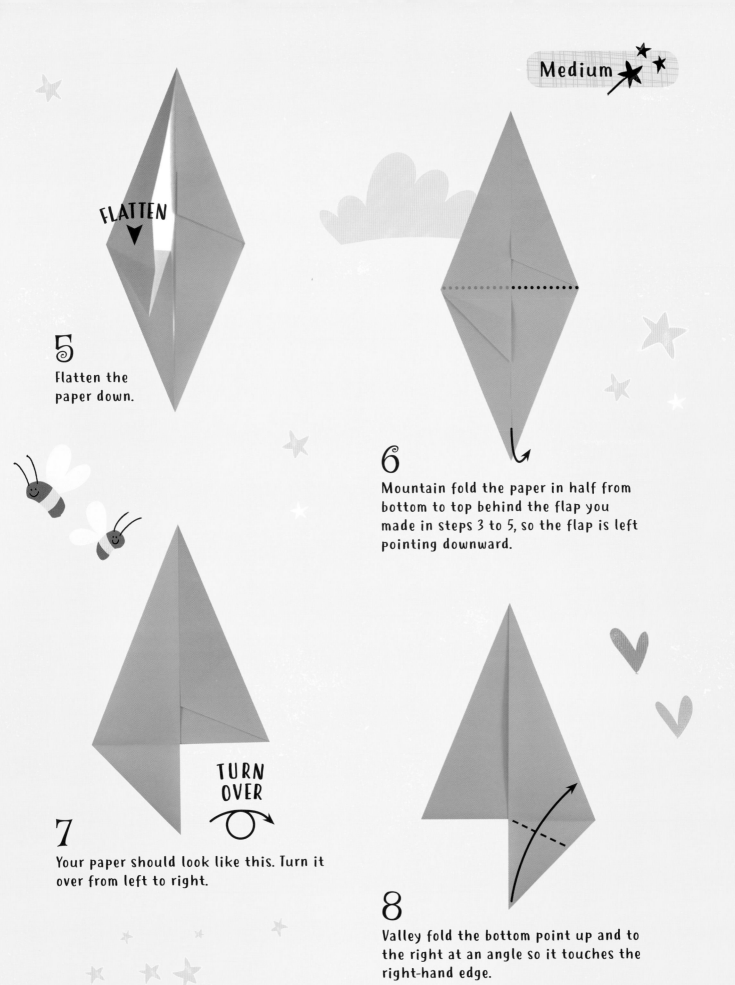

Medium

FLATTEN

5

Flatten the
paper down.

6

Mountain fold the paper in half from
bottom to top behind the flap you
made in steps 3 to 5, so the flap is left
pointing downward.

7

TURN OVER

Your paper should look like this. Turn it
over from left to right.

8

Valley fold the bottom point up and to
the right at an angle so it touches the
right-hand edge.

TURN OVER

9

Turn the paper over from left to right.

10

Valley fold the right-hand point across at an angle, as shown.

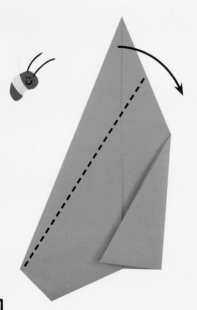

11

Fold the top point of the upper layer down and to the right, so part of it goes over the flap you made in step 10.

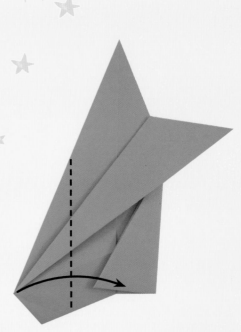

12

Valley fold the bottom left point across so it's roughly in line with the fold you made in step 10. This should reveal the triangle-shaped flap behind it.

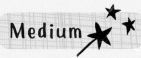

13 ▲ FLATTEN

As you fold, a small flap should form at the bottom of the paper between the new flap and the smaller triangle-shaped flap. Flatten this down.

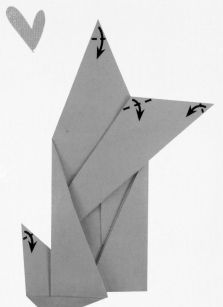

14

Make four small valley folds, as shown.

TURN OVER

15

Make a small valley fold at the bottom, as shown, then turn the paper over from left to right.

16

Your cactus is ready to get some sun. They like it hot.

61

Toadstool Seat

This origami toadstool will make a comfortable seat for a fairy or a unicorn foal. Choose brightly patterned paper to make your toadstool extra magical.

TURN OVER

1

Make a kite base (see page 7) but start with the white side facing down. Your paper should look like this. Turn it over from left to right.

2

Make a mountain fold, as shown, so the bottom point sticks out above the top point.

3 UNFOLD

Unfold the fold you made in step 2.

4

Valley fold the top point down, making the crease in line with the left- and right-hand points.

UNFOLD

5

Unfold the fold you made in step 4.

6

Turn the creases you made in steps 2 and 4 into a step fold.

OPEN

7
Open up the right-hand side and bring the top right point down and to the left.

FLATTEN

8
Flatten your paper down.

9
Your paper should look like this. Repeat steps 7 and 8 on the left-hand side.

10
Valley fold the bottom point.

11
Make three small valley folds, as shown.

TURN OVER

12
Turn the paper over from left to right.

13
And there's your toadstool. Add some decorations to make it as welcoming as possible.

Fluttering Butterfly

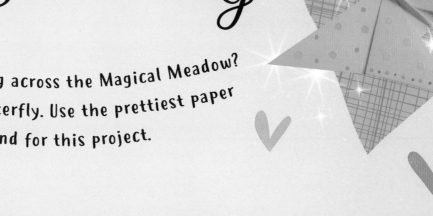

What's this fluttering across the Magical Meadow? It's a beautiful butterfly. Use the prettiest paper you can find for this project.

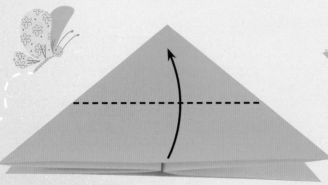

1

Start by making a waterbomb base (see page 8), then valley fold the bottom edge to just below the top point, as shown.

2

Valley fold the top right point of the upper layer down and to the left.

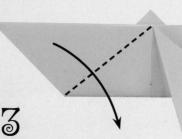

3

Repeat step 2 on the left-hand side. Your butterfly's wings are now complete.

4

Mountain fold the paper in half from left to right.

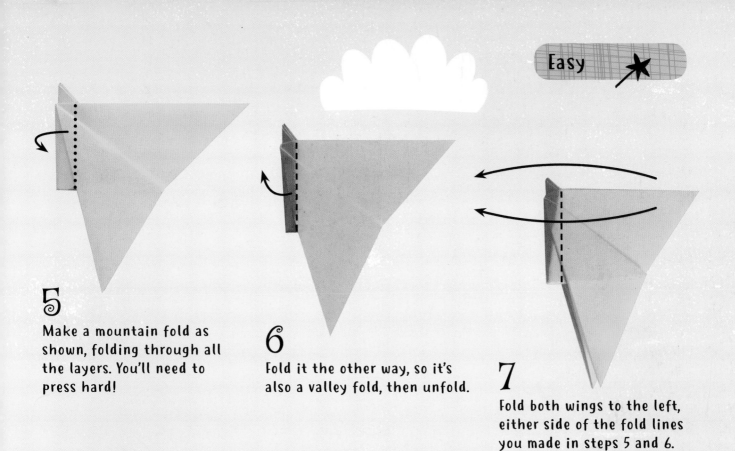

5
Make a mountain fold as shown, folding through all the layers. You'll need to press hard!

6
Fold it the other way, so it's also a valley fold, then unfold.

7
Fold both wings to the left, either side of the fold lines you made in steps 5 and 6.

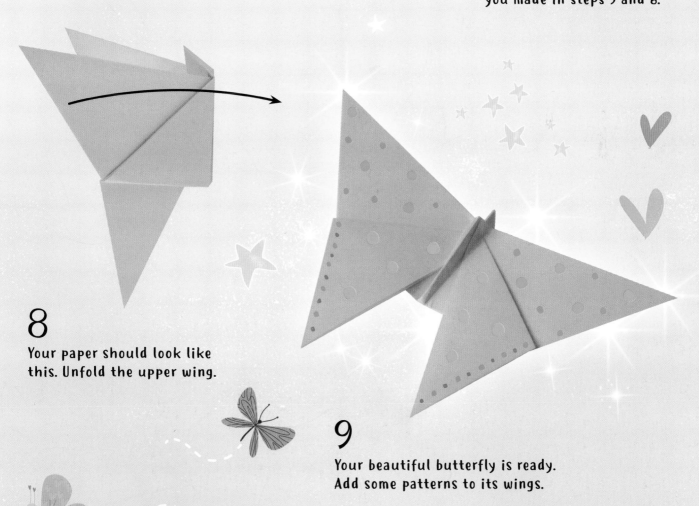

8
Your paper should look like this. Unfold the upper wing.

9
Your beautiful butterfly is ready. Add some patterns to its wings.

65

Beautiful Bird

This bird is a frequent visitor to the Magical Meadow, fluttering over the flowers.

1

Place your paper like this, white side down with a corner facing you. Valley fold it in half from left to right.

2

Valley fold the top right edge of the upper layer over to the central crease.

3

Mountain fold the paper in half from top to bottom.

4

Valley fold the top left-hand corner, but don't flatten it right down.

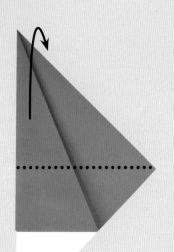

UNFOLD

5

Unfold the fold you made in step 4.

OPEN

6

Open out the paper on the left side. Pull the middle left point of the upper layer up toward the top, keeping it in line with the left-hand edge.

FLATTEN

7

As you pull, the middle right point should start lifting up and coming over to the left, forming a shape like a bird's mouth. Flatten the paper down.

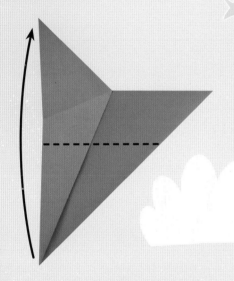

8

Your paper should look like this. Valley fold the bottom point of the upper layer so it lines up with top left point.

9

Mountain fold the bottom point so it lines up with the top point.

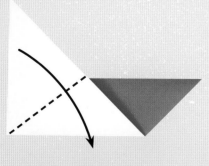

10

Make a diagonal valley fold in the upper layer, as shown, to form the first wing.

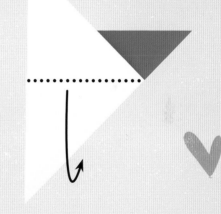

11

Turn the paper over, repeat step 10 on the other side, then turn the paper back over again. Your paper should look like this.

12

Make a valley fold on the right-hand side, then unfold.

13

Fold it the other way, so it's also a mountain fold, then turn it into an outside reverse fold (see page 6).

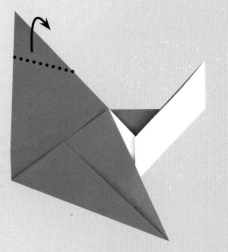

14

Make a mountain fold on the top, as shown.

15

Unfold the fold you made in step 14.

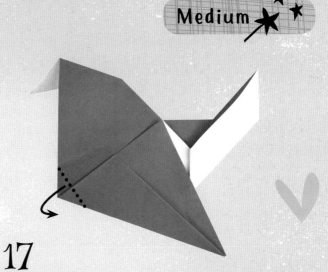

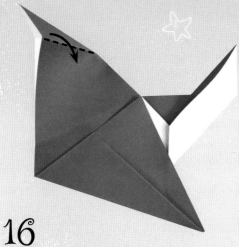

16

Fold it the other way, so it's also a valley fold, then turn it into an inside reverse fold (see page 6).

17

Mountain fold the bottom left point of the upper layer.

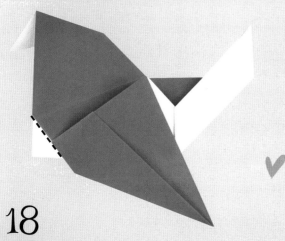

18

Make a matching fold on the other side.

19

Your paper should look like this. Carefully pull the wings apart and your bird should be able to stand up on its wings.

20

You could use different types of paper to create a whole flock of birds for your meadow.

69

Magical Tent

The Magical Meadow is so enchanting, the unicorns will probably want to stay the night. Give them somewhere to stay by making this special tent—with extra room for their horns!

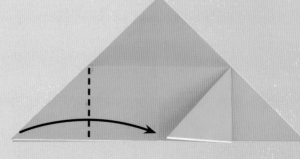

1

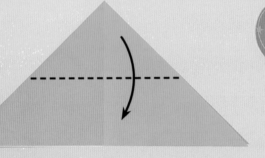

Make a waterbomb base (see page 8). Then valley fold the top point down to the bottom edge.

2

UNFOLD

Unfold the fold you made in step 1.

3

Fold the right-hand point of the upper layer over to the central crease.

4

Repeat step 3 on the left-hand side.

5
Unfold the folds you made in steps 3 and 4.

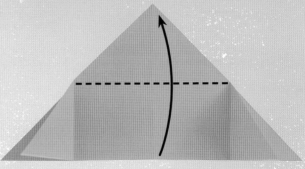

6
Valley fold the bottom edge of the upper layer up to the top point using the crease line you made in step 1. As you do, the left- and right-hand points of the upper layer should start coming across to the central crease.

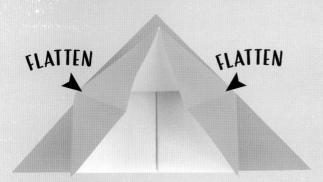

7
Flatten the paper down.

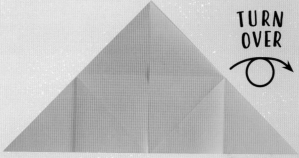

TURN OVER

8
Your paper should look like this. Turn it over from left to right.

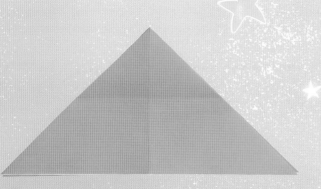

9
Repeat steps 3 to 7 on this side.

10
Make a diagonal valley fold in the upper layer, as shown.

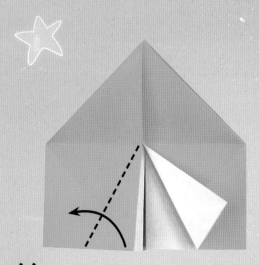

11

Repeat step 10 on the other side.

12

Your paper should look like this. Pick your paper up and gently pull the front and back sections apart, like a concertina.

13

Your tent should be able to stand up on its own.

14

Add some magical decorations and your tent is ready for its first night in the meadow.

72

Unicorn Picnic

Let's finish with a tasty picnic. Follow the instructions to make ice cream cones, cupcakes, slices of watermelon, strawberries, and ice pops—all the unicorns' best-loved treats!

Ice Cream

Time for the unicorns to cool off with a delicious ice cream. Make several so everyone can have one of their own.

1

Start with a kite base (see page 7) positioned like this. Make a diagonal valley fold in the upper layer on the right-hand side to create a new triangle-shaped flap.

2

Make a diagonal valley fold in the upper layer on the left-hand side so it matches the flap made in step 1.

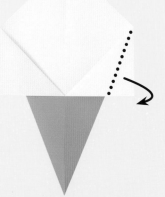

3

Mountain fold the right-hand point behind the paper.

4

Repeat step 3 on the left-hand side.

5

TURN OVER

Turn the paper over from left to right.

6

Valley fold the top-right edge over to the central crease. The new flap will go over the flap you made in step 3.

74

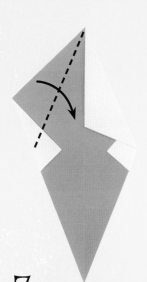

7

Repeat step 6 on the left-hand side.

 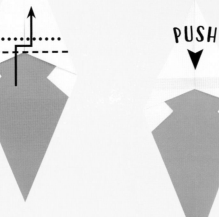

8

Your paper should look like this. Make a step fold in the top half (see page 5) with the valley fold below the mountain fold.

PUSH

9

Push the paper down flat.

TURN OVER

10

Turn the paper over from left to right.

11

Make another step fold nearer the top point, but this time with the mountain fold line below the valley fold line.

PUSH

12

Push the paper down flat.

13

You could add some glittery sprinkles to the top of your ice cream. Then you'd better give it to a unicorn to eat before it melts.

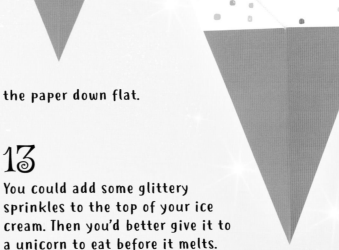

Watermelon

Here's a healthy alternative to ice cream—a slice of watermelon. It's just as refreshing on a hot summer's day.

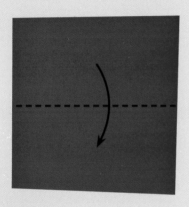

1

Place your paper like this, white side down, with a straight edge facing you. Valley fold in half from top to bottom, and then unfold.

2

Make a small diagonal valley fold in the top-right corner, as shown.

3

Repeat step 2 with the other three corners.

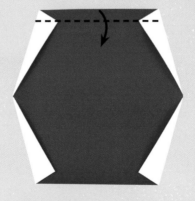

4

Valley fold over the top edge, as shown.

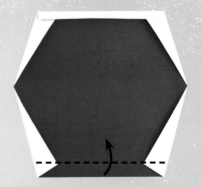

5

Repeat step 4 on the bottom edge.

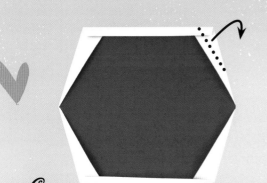

6

Mountain fold the top-right corner, as shown.

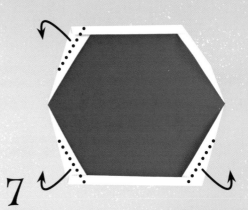

7

Repeat step 6 with the top-left, bottom-left, and bottom-right corners.

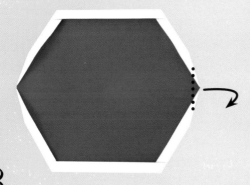

8

Mountain fold the right-hand point, as shown.

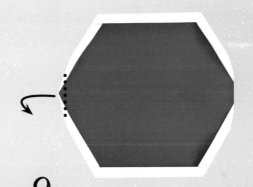

9

Mountain fold the left-hand point.

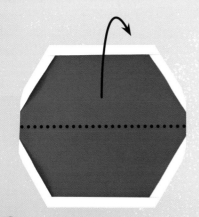

10

Mountain fold the paper in half from top to bottom

11

And there's a tasty slice of watermelon. Use a green pen to draw the rind, and then add in some seeds. Delicious!

Ice Pop

Follow these instructions to make a tasty frozen snack. Be sure to hold it by the stick so your hands don't get too cold! You'll need scissors for this project.

1

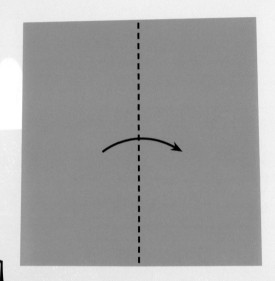

Start with your paper like this, white side down, with a straight edge facing you. Valley fold in half from left to right, and then unfold.

2

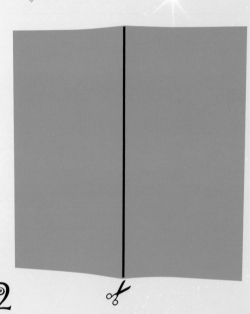

Use scissors to carefully cut your paper in half along the crease line you made in step 1.

3

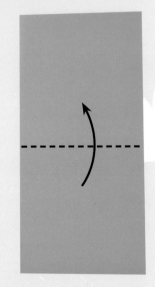

Take one of the pieces of paper and valley fold it in half from bottom to top.

4

UNFOLD

Unfold the fold you made in step 3.

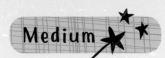

5
Valley fold the bottom edge up to the central crease.

TURN OVER

6
Turn the paper over from left to right.

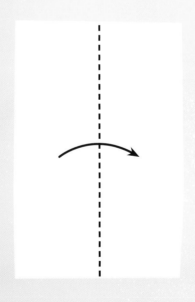

7
Fold the paper in half from left to right.

UNFOLD

8
Unfold the fold you made in step 7.

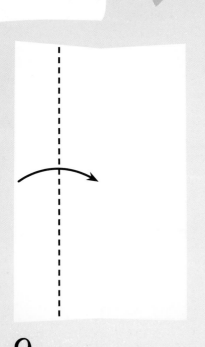

9

Fold the left-hand edge over to the central crease.

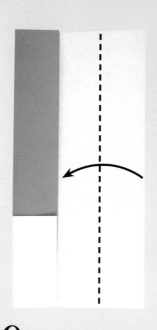

10

Fold the right-hand edge over to the central crease.

11

Make a valley fold, as shown, around three quarters of the way between the left-hand edge and the central line. Don't crease all the way along the paper; just from the bottom edge to slightly above the white area.

UNFOLD

12

Crease well, then unfold.

13

Make a similar fold on the right-hand side, but this time around two thirds of the way between the right-hand edge and the central line, so that, when you fold it, the edge lines up with the crease you made in step 12.

UNFOLD

14

Again, don't crease it all the way, just from the bottom edge to just above the white area. Unfold.

TURN OVER

15

Your paper should look like this. Turn it over from left to right.

16

Valley fold the bottom edge up. Make the crease at the top of the white area.

17

Make a small diagonal valley fold in the bottom corner, as shown, in line with the crease you made in step 11.

18

Repeat step 17 on the left-hand side. Make the crease just slightly farther over than the crease line from step 13, so it matches the fold in step 17.

TURN OVER

19

Turn your paper over from left to right.

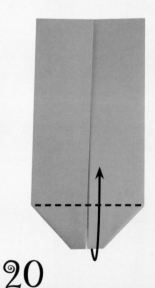

20

Make a horizontal valley fold at the bottom of the paper, as shown. Flip the lower layer forward so the white area appears again at the bottom of the paper.

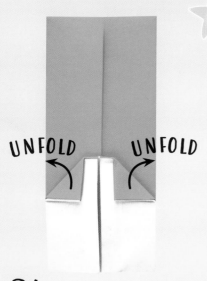

UNFOLD   UNFOLD

21

Your paper should look like
this. Unfold the folds you
made in steps 17 and 18.

OPEN

22

Open out the white area
at the top on the right-
hand side.

PUSH

23

Push the top-right point
down and to the left so it
forms a triangle shape. This
should make the paper fold
over along the line of the
fold you made in step 13.

FLATTEN

24

Flatten the triangle shape down.

FLATTEN

25

Your paper should look like
this. Repeat steps 22 and 23
on the left-hand side.

FLATTEN

26

Flatten the triangle
shape down.

27
Valley fold the top-right point, as shown.

28
Repeat step 27 on the left-hand side.

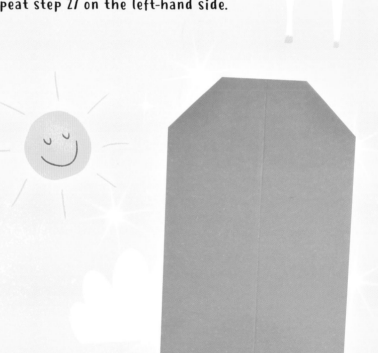

TURN OVER

29
Turn your paper over from left to right.

30
That's one ice pop made. Make sure you do enough for everyone.

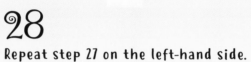

Strawberry

Here's how to make an origami strawberry, the perfect summer fruit. All magical (and non-magical) creatures love them.

1
Place your paper like this, white side up, with a corner facing you. Valley fold it in half from top to bottom.

2
Valley fold the paper in half from right to left.

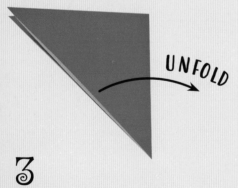

UNFOLD

3
Unfold the fold you made in step 2.

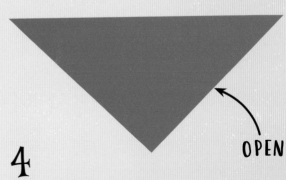

OPEN

4
Open up the paper on the right-hand side, so it forms a shape a bit like a bird's mouth.

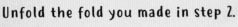

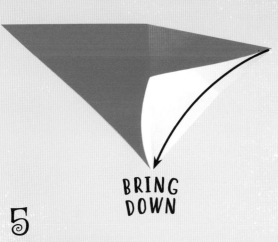

BRING DOWN

5

Bring the top-right point down to the bottom point. Flatten the paper down.

TURN OVER

6

Your paper should look like this. Turn it over from left to right.

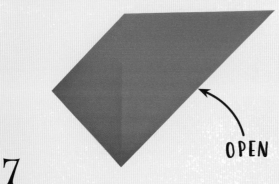

OPEN

7

Open up the paper on the right-hand side.

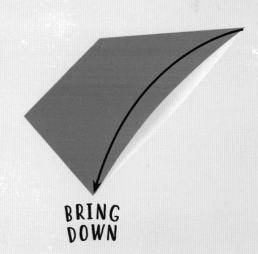

BRING DOWN

8

Repeat step 5, bringing the top-right point down to the bottom point, then flattening the paper.

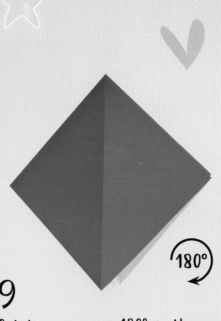

9

Rotate your paper 180°, so the open points are at the top.

10

Mountain fold the top point of the upper layer, as shown.

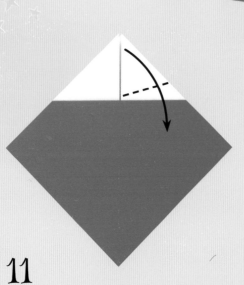

11

Valley fold the top point of the new upper layer down and to the right, as shown.

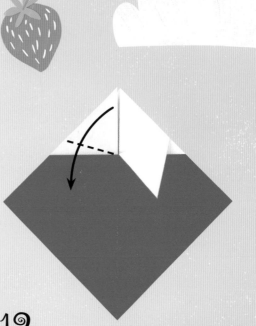

12

Repeat step 11 on the left-hand side.

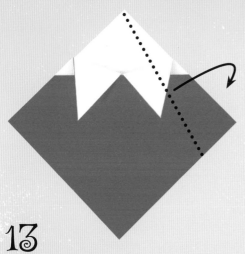

13

Make a mountain fold on the right-hand side, as shown. Crease well.

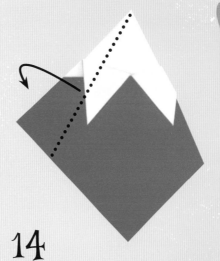

14

Repeat step 13 on the left-hand side.

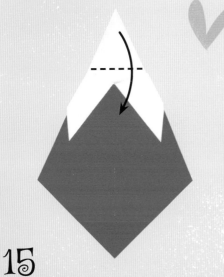

15

Valley fold over the top point.

16

Add some seeds, decorate the leaves, and your strawberry is ready. It looks good enough to eat!

Treat Box

You'll need something to carry your sweet treats in, so grab a piece of paper to make this cute, candylike box.

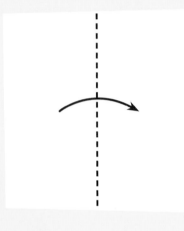

1

Place your paper like this, white side up with a straight edge facing you. Valley fold it in half from left to right, then unfold.

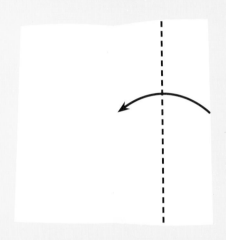

2

Valley fold the right-hand edge over to the central crease.

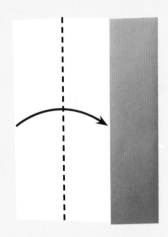

3

Valley fold the left-hand edge over to the central crease.

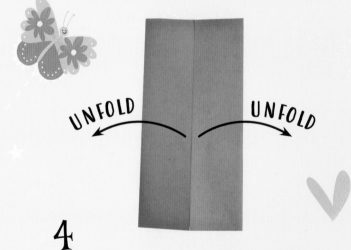

4

Open up the folds you made in steps 2 and 3.

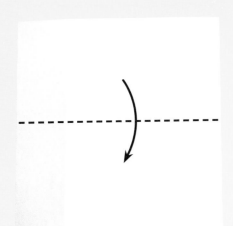

5
Valley fold the paper in half from top to bottom.

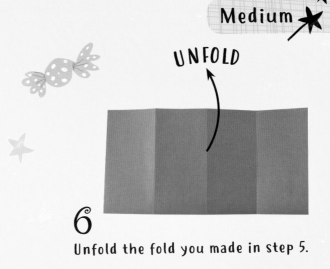

UNFOLD

6
Unfold the fold you made in step 5.

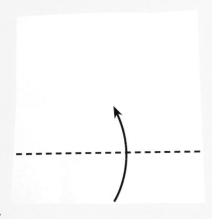

7
Your paper should look like this. Valley fold the bottom edge up to the central crease.

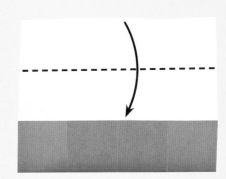

8
Valley fold the top edge down to the central crease.

TURN OVER

9
Turn your paper over from left to right.

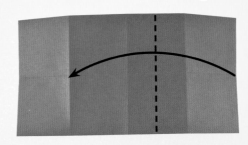

10
Valley fold the right-hand edge over to the vertical crease line nearest the left-hand edge.

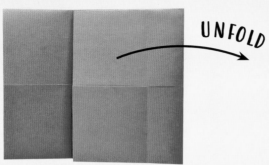

UNFOLD

11

Unfold the fold you made in step 10.

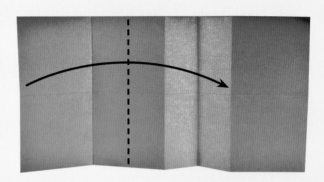

12

Valley fold the left-hand edge over to the vertical crease nearest the right-hand edge.

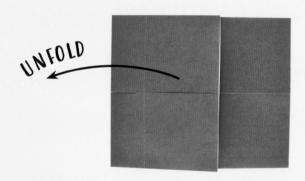

UNFOLD

13

Unfold the fold you made in step 12.

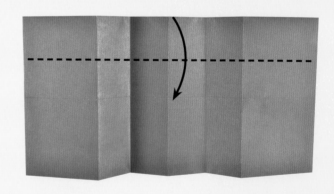

14

Valley fold the top edge down to the central crease.

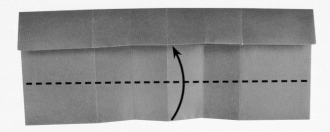

15

Valley fold the bottom edge up to the central crease.

TURN OVER

16

Turn the paper over from left to right.

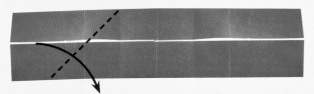

17

Make a diagonal valley fold, as shown, by folding the top-left corner down and to the right so it lines up with the crease line second from the left.

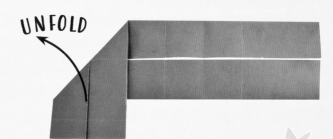

UNFOLD

18

Unfold the fold you made in step 17.

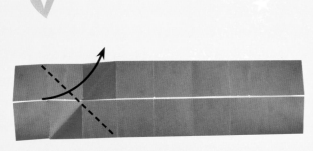

19

Repeat step 17 the other way, folding the bottom-left corner up and to the right so it lines up with the crease line second from the left.

UNFOLD

20

Unfold the fold you made in step 19.

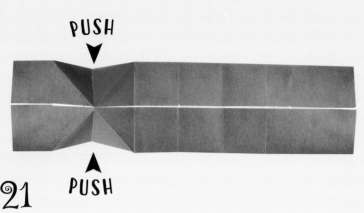

PUSH

PUSH

21

Your paper should look like this. Press in the paper either side of the crease lines you made in steps 17 and 19. This should form two triangle shapes.

PUSH

BRING OVER

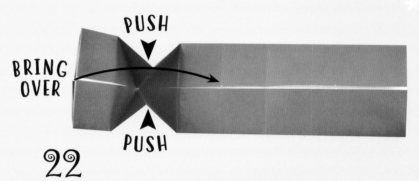

PUSH

22

Keep pushing so the triangle shapes almost touch. This should bring the left-hand edge up and over to the right. Bring the left-hand edge all the way over to the right and flatten it down.

OPEN

OPEN

23

Your paper should look like this. Open up the flaps of the upper layer on the left-hand side.

PULL

PULL

24

Pull the points apart, as shown, so the flap below them is sticking straight up toward you.

FLATTEN

25

Flatten down so it looks like the picture in step 26.

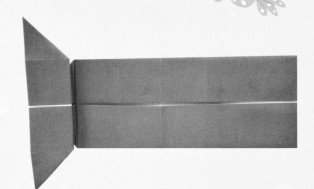

26

Repeat steps 17 to 25 on the right-hand side.

TURN OVER

27

Turn your paper over from left to right.

OPEN

OPEN

OPEN

OPEN

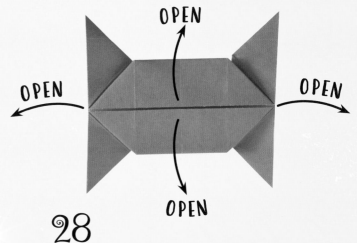

28

Open out the middle and end sections so the paper forms a box.

29

Your treat box is complete. But what will you put inside? Something to tempt a unicorn, perhaps?

Cupcake

No picnic is complete without cupcakes!
Get lots of sheets of paper so you can
make cakes of all different types.

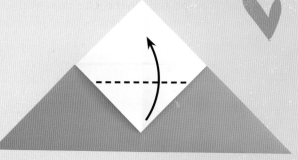

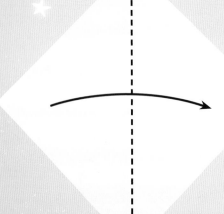

1

Place your paper like this, white side up,
with a corner facing you. Valley fold in half
from left to right, then unfold.

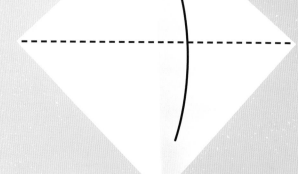

2

Valley fold your paper in half from
bottom to top.

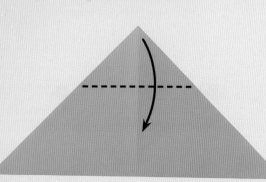

3

Valley fold the top point of the upper layer
about a third of the way from the top.

4

Valley fold the point up again, as shown.

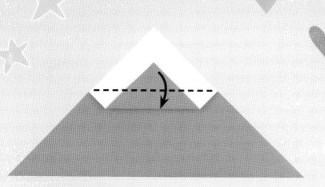

5

Valley fold the point again, in line with the crease you made in step 3.

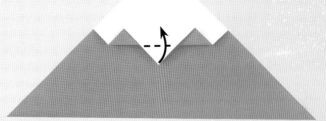

6

Valley fold the point one more time in line with the crease you made in step 4.

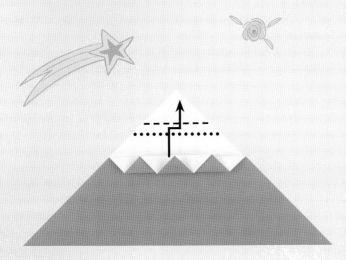

7

Make a step fold at the top of the paper (see page 5) with the mountain fold below the valley fold.

FLATTEN

8

Flatten the paper down.

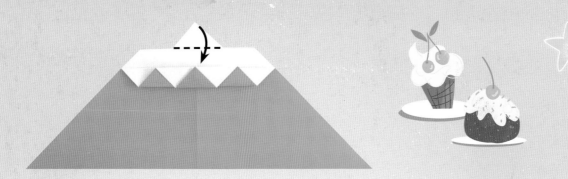

9

Valley fold the top point over the layer above it, as shown.

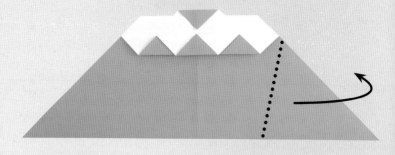

10

Mountain fold the right-hand side at an angle.

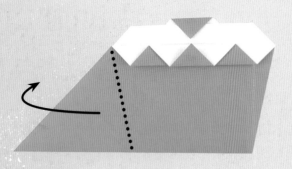

11

Repeat step 10 on the left-hand side.

12

That's your first cupcake baked! Why not use it with your cake topper from chapter 1?